Skills Builders

Grammar and Punctuation

YEAR
3

Maddy Barnes

RISING STARS

Rising Stars UK Ltd, 7 Hatchers Mews, Bermondsey Street, London SE1 3GS
www.risingstars-uk.com

Every effort has been made to trace copyright holders and obtain their permission for the use of copyright materials. The publishers will gladly receive information enabling them to rectify any error or omission in subsequent editions.

All facts are correct at time of going to press.

Published 2013
Reprinted 2013
Text, design and layout © 2013 Rising Stars UK Ltd

Project manager: Dawn Booth
Editorial: Sue Walton
Proofreader: Margaret Crowther
Design: Words & Pictures Ltd, London
Cover design: Amina Dudhia
Acknowledgements: p.7 iStock/Eric Isselée; p.9 iStock/sureyya akin;
p.12 Dave Thompson; p.14 iStock/Tracie Andrews; p.15 iStock/Aritisticco LLC;
p.17 iStock/Daniel Villeneuve; p.18 iStock/Anton Brand; p.19 iStock/peanutpie;
p.25 Dave Thompson; p.27 iStock/Servet Gűrbűz; p.28 iStock/Waiale
p.30 iStock/Dan Møller; p.34 iStock/ssstep; p.35 iStock/Anton Brand;
p.39 iStock/shiny77777; p.44 iStock/sekerlili

British Library Cataloguing-in-Publication Data
A CIP record for this book is available from the British Library.

ISBN: 978-0-85769-694-6
Printed in Singapore by Craft Print International

Skills Builders: Grammar and Punctuation

YEAR
3

Contents

* Revision pages

How to use this book

What we have included:

1 Each unit covers aspects of grammar and punctuation taken from the new National Curriculum framework.

2 The units at the beginning of the book focus on basic skills which pupils should recognise from their previous learning and set mini challenges to encourage pupils to recap what they already know. These are often 'Warming up' questions, which are also used to test just learned knowledge throughout the book.

3 Other sections introduce new skills which are organised in a 'Getting hotter' section and some push even further in the 'Burn it up!' section.

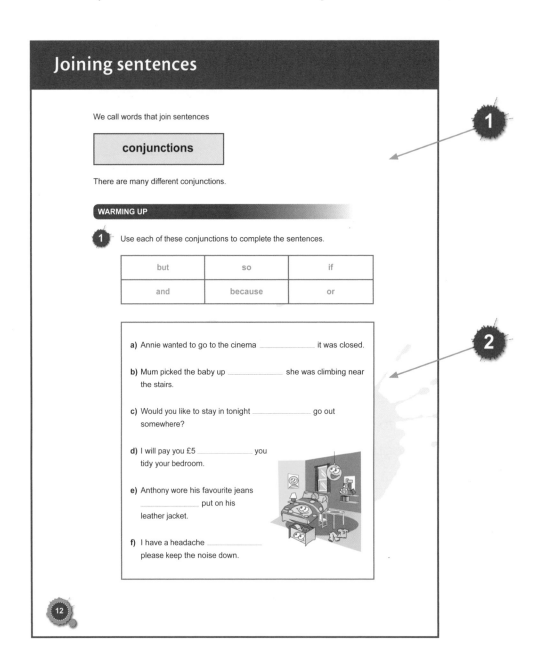

Joining sentences

We call words that join sentences

conjunctions

There are many different conjunctions.

WARMING UP

1 Use each of these conjunctions to complete the sentences.

but	so	if
and	because	or

a) Annie wanted to go to the cinema _____ it was closed.

b) Mum picked the baby up _____ she was climbing near the stairs.

c) Would you like to stay in tonight _____ go out somewhere?

d) I will pay you £5 _____ you tidy your bedroom.

e) Anthony wore his favourite jeans _____ put on his leather jacket.

f) I have a headache _____ please keep the noise down.

12

1

2

How to use this book

4 At the end of each section is a 'How did I do?' assessment for learning where pupils can record how well they did.

5 There are assessment points throughout the book titled 'Assess and review', which allow opportunities for pupils to recap new learning in small steps.

6 The correct grammatical terminology is used throughout this book to encourage acquisition of technical language.

7 All answers are included so pupils can check on their progress.

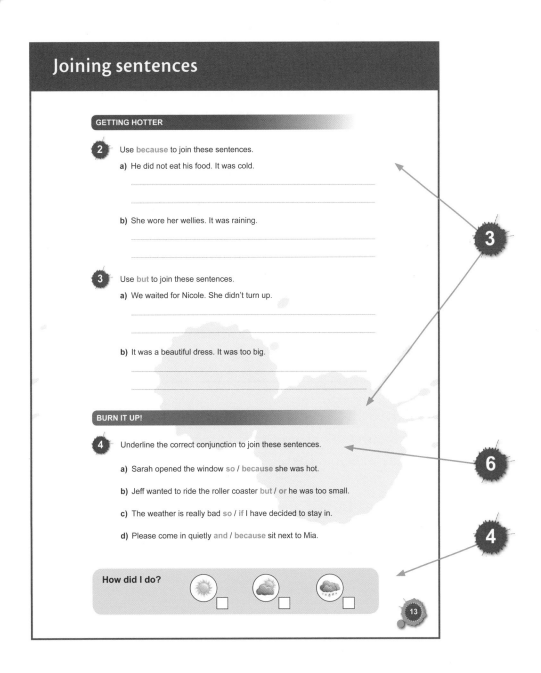

Using punctuation and capital letters

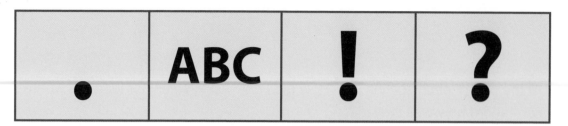

When we write sentences, we need to use capital letters in the correct places and end them with a punctuation mark.

WARMING UP

 1 Complete these sentences with the correct punctuation.

a) What time are we having lunch _____

b) Give it to me _____

c) wing Gee wore a pink dress and shiny black shoes _____

d) come in _____

e) What is your favourite colour _____

GETTING HOTTER

2 Change these statements into questions. The first word has been given to help you.

a) You are late. Will _____ ?

b) I want to play with you. Can _____ ?

c) This film is great. Do _____ ?

How did I do? ☐ ☐ ☐

Using commas in a list

When we write lists we separate each item in the list with a comma.

> The bird is blue, yellow, red, green and black.
>
> People usually live in houses, flats, bungalows or caravans.

 1 Add a comma or commas to the following sentences.

> **a)** I use a knife fork and spoon to eat with.
>
> **b)** I like listening to pop rock and disco music.
>
> **c)** Faye likes to wear sandals trainers boots and shoes.
>
> **d)** John enjoys maths science art and PE.
>
> **e)** My friends are Claire Jade Laura Bal and Louisa.
>
> **f)** Tim plays football rounders tennis golf and basketball.

How did I do?

 □ □ □

Using apostrophes accurately

We use an apostrophe to show:

Possession	Contraction
To show that somebody owns something.	When words are shortened and letters are missed out.
Pete's boat the cat's bowl the computer's wire	I'm can't won't

WARMING UP

 1 Read the sentences below and decide if the apostrophe shows possession (**P**) or contraction (**C**).

I don't know what to do today.	
Samuel's eyes are blue.	
I haven't got time to go swimming.	
I am cleaning my Dad's car.	
This is my sister's calculator.	
I couldn't do my homework last night.	
The bike's wheel is broken.	
The teacher's pen fell onto the floor.	

How did I do?

Proper nouns, nouns, verbs and adjectives

These are some of the different word classes. Can you remember what they do?

Proper nouns	Nouns	Verbs	Adjectives
Words for people, pets and places.	Words for animals, people and things.	Tell us what is happening in a sentence.	Tell us more about a noun.
Dermot Wendy India Scotland	elephant teacher table book	running ate asked wear	huge cute two brown

WARMING UP

 1 Underline the verb and circle the proper noun in these sentences.

a) Daniel ate his apple.

b) Eleanor ran to school.

c) They drove to Scotland.

GETTING HOTTER

 2 Underline the adjectives in these sentences.

a) The silver car was very fast.

b) The sun was bright and hot.

c) We sailed to a deserted beach.

d) The boat had a blue and white stripy sail.

How did I do?

Singular and plural

When we change singular nouns to plural nouns we add -s. However, if the noun ends with s, ch, sh, x or z then we add -es.

Singular noun	Plural noun
plate	plates
glass	glasses
phone	phones
curtain	curtains
lunch	lunches
switch	switches
sash	sashes
fox	foxes
quiz	quizzes

WARMING UP

 1 Complete the gaps in the table below.

Singular	Plural
hair	
	witches
card	
	benches
bag	
	catches
chair	

How did I do? ☐ ☐ ☐

Expanded noun phrases

Adjectives tell you more about nouns. We choose powerful adjectives to add more detail for better descriptions. Adjectives can come before or after the noun.

> The **small**, **cute** kitten
>
> or
>
> the kitten was **small** and **cute**.

We can create expanded noun phrases and write longer sentences by using adjectives. Here are some categories we could use:

Appearance	Colour	Feelings
clean	blue	jealous
beautiful	pink	grumpy
sparkling	turquoise	scary
tall	violet	excited

WARMING UP

 1 Underline the correct adjective to complete each of these sentences.

a) I had a **hot** / **short** drink with my cake.

b) This winter it was very **pink** / **cold**.

c) The ice cream had a **sweet** / **scary** taste to it.

d) The dog gave a **sparkling** / **loud** yelp.

e) The giraffe is very **green** / **tall**.

How did I do? ☐ ☐ ☐

Joining sentences

We call words that join sentences

conjunctions

There are many different conjunctions.

 1 Use each of these conjunctions to complete the sentences.

but	so	if
and	because	or

a) Annie wanted to go to the cinema _____ it was closed.

b) Mum picked the baby up _____ she was climbing near the stairs.

c) Would you like to stay in tonight _____ go out somewhere?

d) I will pay you £5 _____ you tidy your bedroom.

e) Anthony wore his favourite jeans _____ put on his leather jacket.

f) I have a headache _____ please keep the noise down.

Joining sentences

2 Use **because** to join these sentences.

a) He did not eat his food. It was cold.

....

....

b) She wore her wellies. It was raining.

....

....

3 Use **but** to join these sentences.

a) We waited for Nicole. She didn't turn up.

....

....

b) It was a beautiful dress. It was too big.

....

....

BURN IT UP!

4 Underline the correct conjunction to join these sentences.

a) Sarah opened the window **so** / **because** she was hot.

b) Jeff wanted to ride the roller coaster **but** / **or** he was too small.

c) The weather is really bad **so** / **if** I have decided to stay in.

d) Please come in quietly **and** / **because** sit next to Mia.

How did I do?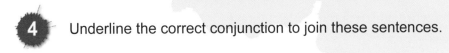

13

Past and present tense

Verbs can be written in the past tense (what has already happened) or the present tense (what is happening now).

Past tense: The dog **ran** to the park.

Present tense: The dog **runs** to the park.

WARMING UP

 1 Read the sentences below and label them with the correct tense. Choose past or present.

a) The boys enjoyed the film. _____

b) The birds flew in the sky. _____

c) The teacher is sitting at her table. _____

d) My friends are playing in the park. _____

e) Gran baked a beautiful cake. _____

f) He cleaned the car and polished it too. _____

GETTING HOTTER

 2 Circle the word which is the correct tense for each sentence.

a) He **painted** / **painting** the house yesterday.

b) The baby is **cried** / **crying** in her pram.

c) The girls were **reading** / **read** in the library.

d) Last Tuesday Dylan **is cycling** / **cycled** to school.

e) After we ate our dinner we **drank** / **are drinking** our milk.

How did I do?

 ☐   ☐   ☐

Vowels and consonants

The alphabet is organised into vowels and consonants.

Vowels	a e i o u
Consonants	b c d f g h j k l m n p q r s t v w x y z

 1 Write the consonants which are in each word.
For example: apple   p p l

a) doctor

b) school

c) boat

d) clock

e) radio

f) zoo

g) shopkeeper

h) ice cream

i) sweeping brush

How did I do?

What is a sentence?

Usually sentences have a subject and a verb:

> The boy ran.   Subject = boy   Verb = ran
>
> The girl sang.   Subject = girl   Verb = sang

We can make sentences longer in different ways:

➤ by adding more detail:

> The boy ran **quickly to the shop**.
>
> The girl sang **like a beautiful bird**.

➤ by adding joining words:

> The boy ran to the shop **and** bought some sweets.
>
> The girl sang **but** she was not very good!

There are different types of sentences:

Statements	It was sunny today. I saw a big, scary dog near the post office.	.
Questions	Do you know him? Have you seen the film?	?
Exclamations	Oh dear! I cannot believe you!	!

What is a sentence?

A **command** is telling somebody to do something in a firm way.

When somebody gives a **command** they usually do not use a subject. They do not need a subject because the subject is obvious – you!

Commands	**Stop it!** **Look!** **Watch it!**	**!** or ●

1 Read the following sentences and label them:
statements (**S**), questions (**Q**), exclamations (**E**) and commands (**C**).

How old are you Peter?	
Give it to me!	
You are the worst singer I have ever heard!	
There are too many people in here.	
Wait a minute!	
Do you know that teacher's name?	
Yes, yes, we won!	

How did I do?

 ☐   ☐   ☐

17

Simple sentences and clauses

How do we know what a clause is?

    ✓ **a single idea or event,**

    ✓ **has one verb,**

    ✓ **has a subject.**

> **A simple sentence = one clause.**

The boy read a book.

subject   **verb**

WARMING UP

 1   Tick the sentences which have one clause.

The girl woke up and she went downstairs.	
The lion chased the deer.	
He was wearing his football kit.	
The doctor gave the woman some medicine.	
The boy took the dog for a walk.	

How did I do?   □   □   □

Assess and review

 1 Put these words into the correct word classes.

short	eat	chair	Phoebe	skip

short   eat   chair   Phoebe   skip
sweet   book   fat   write
Germany   orange   walk
blue
dog   Liverpool   Robert

Proper nouns	Nouns	Verbs	Adjectives

2 Complete each sentence with the correct punctuation.

a) Mum .... s car is black and silver.

b) Why don .... t you play in the garden ....

c) I won, I won, I won ....

d) I need to buy apples .... oranges .... grapes .... bananas
and strawberries for the fruit salad.

e) That isn .... t fair, I did my best ....

Assess and review

3 Write the beginnings for these sentences.

a) _____

so I could eat my breakfast.

b) _____

but he didn't know why.

c) _____

and we played all day there.

d) _____

because it was snowing heavily.

e) _____

or cottage pie for your dinner?

4 Count how many consonants and vowels are in each word.

a) kitchen _____

b) skateboard _____

c) magazine _____

d) cricket _____

e) umbrella _____

f) butterfly _____

g) machine _____

Assess and review

5 Complete the gaps in the table below:

Singular nouns	Plural nouns
house	
banana	
	tables
lunch	
	dashes
	witches
	phones
box	
fizz	

6 Add some adjectives to the following nouns to create expended noun phrases.

The first one has been done for you.

the chair	the old wooden chair near the window
the dog	
the man	
the car	
the tree	
the sandwich	
the apple	

How did I do?

Adding prefixes

A **prefix** is added at the beginning of a word to make another word.

These prefixes all change the words in a similar way and have negative meanings:

un-	dis-	mis-
happy **unhappy**	appear **disappear**	placed **misplaced**

WARMING UP

 1 Read these words and decide which prefix you can add to them:
un-, dis- or mis-.

a) ....appoint   b) ....understand

c) ....agree   d) ....known

e) ....aware   f) ....available

g) ....honest   h) ....comfortable

GETTING HOTTER

 2 Underline four words which have been misspelled.

misteak   dissappear   disagree

undecided   unnknown

unaware

missplaced   dishonest

Answers

Skills Builders

Grammar and Punctuation

YEAR 3

Maddy Barnes

Using punctuation and capital letters (page 6)

1 a) ? b) ! c) Wing, . d) Come, ! e) ?

2 a) Will you be late? b) Can I play with you?

   c) Do you think this film is great?

Using commas in a list (page 7)

1 a) I use a knife, fork and spoon to eat with.

   b) I like listening to pop, rock and disco music.

   c) Faye likes to wear sandals, trainers, boots and shoes.

   d) John enjoys maths, science, art and PE.

   e) My friends are Claire, Jade, Laura, Bal and Louisa.

   f) Tim plays football, rounders, tennis, golf and basketball.

Using apostrophes accurately (page 8)

1

I don't know what to do today.	C
Samuel's eyes are blue.	P
I haven't got time to go swimming.	C
I am cleaning my Dad's car.	P
This is my sister's calculator.	P
I couldn't do my homework last night.	C
The bike's wheel is broken.	P
The teacher's pen fell onto the floor.	P

Proper nouns, nouns, verbs and adjectives (page 9)

1 a) Daniel ate his apple.

   b) Eleanor ran to school.

   c) They drove to Scotland.

2 a) The silver car was very fast.

   b) The sun was bright and hot.

   c) We sailed to a deserted beach.

   d) The boat had a blue and white stripy sail.

Singular and plural (page 10)

1

Singular	Plural
hair	hairs
witch	witches
card	cards
bench	benches
bag	bags
catch	catches
chair	chairs

Expanded noun phrases (page 11)

1 a) I had a hot / short drink with my cake.

   b) This winter it was very pink / cold.

   c) The ice cream had a sweet / scary taste to it.

   d) The dog gave a sparkling / loud yelp.

   e) The giraffe is very green / tall.

Joining sentences (pages 12–13)

1 a) but b) because c) or d) if e) and f) so

2 a) He did not eat his food because it was cold.

   b) She wore her wellies because it was raining.

3 a) We waited for Nicole but she didn't turn up.

   b) It was a beautiful dress but it was too big.

4 a) Sarah opened the window so / because she was hot.

   b) Jeff wanted to ride the roller coaster but / or he was too small.

   c) The weather is really bad so / if I have decided to stay in.

   d) Please come in quietly and / because sit next to Mia.

Past and present tense (page 14)

1 a) past b) past c) present d) present e) past f) past

2 a) He painted / painting the house yesterday.

   b) The baby is cried / crying in her pram.

   c) The girls were reading / read in the library.

   d) Last Tuesday Dylan is cycling / cycled to school.

   e) After we ate our dinner we drank / are drinking our milk.

Vowels and consonants (page 15)

1 a) d c t r b) s c h l c) b t d) c l c k e) r d f) z

   g) s h p k p r h) c c r m i) s w p n g b r s h

What is a sentence? (page 17)

1

How old are you Peter?	Q
Give it to me!	C
You are the worst singer I have ever heard!	E
There are too many people in here.	S
Wait a minute!	C
Do you know that teacher's name?	Q
Yes, yes, we won!	E

Simple sentences and clauses (page 18)

1

The girl woke up and she went downstairs.	
The lion chased the deer.	✓
He was wearing his football kit.	✓
The doctor gave the woman some medicine.	✓
The boy took the dog for a walk.	✓

Assess and review (pages 19–21)

1

Proper nouns	Nouns	Verbs	Adjectives
Phoebe	chair	eat	short
Germany	orange (or adjective)	skip	blue
Robert	dog	walk (or noun)	fat
Liverpool	book	write	sweet (or noun)

2 **a)** Mum's car is black and silver.

  b) Why don't you play in the garden?

  c) I won, I won, I won!

  d) I need to buy apples, oranges, grapes, bananas and strawberries for the fruit salad.

  e) That isn't fair, I did my best!

3 Answers will vary

  a) I washed my hands **b)** Abdul asked John **c)** We went to the park

  d) We didn't go to school **e)** Would you prefer curry

4 **a)** 5C, 2V **b)** 6C, 4V **c)** 4C, 4V **d)** 5C, 2V **e)** 5C, 3V **f)** 7C, 2V

  g) 4C, 3V

5

Singular nouns	Plural nouns
house	houses
banana	bananas
table	tables
lunch	lunches
dash	dashes
witch	witches
phone	phones
box	boxes
fizz	fizzes

6

the dog	the black and white spotty Dalmatian dog
the man	the tall, thin man with brown hair
the car	the blue, shiny sports car at the garage
the tree	the bent wishing tree near the cottage
the sandwich	the mouldy green sandwich in the bin
the apple	the rosy red apple in my hand

Adding prefixes (pages 22–23)

1 **a)** disappoint **b)** misunderstand **c)** disagree **d)** unknown

  e) unaware **f)** unavailable **g)** dishonest **h)** uncomfortable

2 **a)** misteak **b)** missplaced **c)** dissappear **d)** unnknown

3 **a)** superstar **b)** rewrite **c)** anticlockwise **d)** recharge

  e) superpower **f)** antibiotic **g)** recycle **h)** antiseptic

  i) supernatural

4

misbehave	✓	antiuncle	✗
unfair	✓	untable	✗
misread	✓	reform	✓
supermoney	✗	misruler	✗
retype	✓	unequal	✓

Using determiners (pages 24–25)

1 **a)** a balloon **b)** a car **c)** a robot **d)** a mango **e)** an egg **f)** an ant

  g) an ice cream **h)** an octopus **i)** a kettle

2 **a)** Both **b)** another **c)** other **d)** This **e)** my

3 **a)** I would like either <u>an</u> apple or <u>a</u> pear.

  b) <u>Both</u> singers were very good tonight.

  c) <u>The</u> other bike was much faster.

  d) <u>His</u> school report was not very good.

  e) How was <u>your</u> holiday?

Using time conjunctions (page 26)

1 **a)** I promise I will phone you <u>when</u> / until I get there.

  b) All of the cakes had gone <u>by the time</u> / while I got to the party.

  c) Freddie waited at the station <u>until</u> / as soon as the diesel train arrived.

  d) <u>Before</u> / as soon as I go to bed I will brush my teeth.

  e) I will play cards with you <u>after</u> / by the time I have had my bath.

Using adverbs of time (page 27)

1 **a)** soon **b)** then **c)** today **d)** during **e)** recently

2 **a)** I'm going to school (soon)

  b) Would you like to go (next)?

  c) (Yesterday) I bought a new school bag.

  d) I woke up five times (during) the night.

  e) We've been to the zoo (today)

What is a preposition? (page 28)

1 **a)** onto **b)** under **c)** next to **d)** through

Using prepositions accurately (page 29)

1 **a)** Before **b)** During **c)** Following or After **d)** except **e)** After or Following

  f) because of or following or after

Assess and review (pages 30–31)

1 **a)** misbehave **b)** unnatural or supernatural **c)** undecided **d)** return

  e) untie **f)** repay **g)** remove **h)** discontinue **i)** refill

  j) antifreeze or refreeze **k)** retake or mistake **l)** replay

2 **a)** a **b)** an **c)** an **d)** a **e)** an **f)** a **g)** a **h)** a **i)** a **j)** an **k)** an **l)** a

3 **a)** before **b)** until **c)** after **d)** before

4 Any ten from: in, up, with, round, over, on top, after, through, under, inside, an, next to, under, beside, behind, beneath, before, after, following, during, because of, except

Titles and subheadings (pages 32–33)

1 **a)** A Guide to London **b)** Ugly Duckling? **c)** All About Drumming

2 Answers will vary

    a) Where rabbits live **b)** What rabbits eat **c)** How rabbits exercise

How do we organise our writing? (pages 34–35)

1 **a)** O **b)** O **c)** E **d)** E

2 **a)** 2 **b)** 4 **c)** 3

Using pronouns to vary the subject (page 36)

1 Cara was really excited about starting ballet lessons. She had looked forward to this day. She put her ballet kit in her new bag. Cara was ready to go and she was excited.

2 **a)** Jacob put his shoes on by <u>himself</u> / his.

    b) Mum and Dad bought <u>her</u> / she a new phone.

    c) Everybody blames <u>me</u> / my for everything.

    d) I wonder if <u>he</u> / me will score a goal.

Punctuating direct speech (pages 38–39)

1 **a)** "What big teeth you have Grandma!" said Little Red Riding Hood.

    b) "All the better to eat you with!" screamed the wolf.

2 **a)** "What would you like to eat for lunch?" asked Mum.

    b) "I would like a ham, cheese and tomato sandwich please Mum," said Kirsty.

    c) "Your sandwich is ready Kirsty, come and get it please," called Mum.

    d) "Thanks Mum, you are the best!" smiled Kirsty.

Present perfect form of verbs (pages 40–41)

1 **a)** He <u>has</u> never <u>been</u> to a theme park.

    b) The rain <u>hasn't stopped</u> all day.

    c) I <u>have had</u> so much to eat today.

    d) We <u>have had</u> three tests this week already.

2 **a)** have visited **b)** has visited **c)** have arrested **d)** has melted

3 **a)** has written **b)** has been **c)** have taken **d)** has ridden **e)** have gone

    f) have taken

Conjunctions and connectives (page 42)

1 Beginning: it all began, yesterday Middle: next, then, first, after that, in a flash, so, when Ending: finally, at last, it was the end

Assess and review (pages 43–44)

1 **a)** "My legs are really hurting," cried Nadien.

    b) "I want to go and see the train at the station," said Freddie.

    c) "Come on, let's go and play!" exclaimed Bal.

    d) "Somebody help, please, HELP!" screamed the old lady.

2 **a)** he **b)** my **c)** they **d)** her **e)** your **f)** his

3 **a)** I have seen this film before.

    b) My Mum has washed my clothes for me.

    c) He has finished his homework before everybody else.

    d) She has visited Greece before.

    e) Dad has cooked dinner for everybody.

    f) The florist has arranged the wedding flowers beautifully.

    g) We have known the Flanagans for years.

    h) I have waited over an hour for a bus.

Adding prefixes

These prefixes all have different meanings:

super-	anti-	re-
means above	means against	means again or back
superman	**antifreeze**	**rearrange**

BURN IT UP!

3 Add the correct prefix to these words.
Choose from **super-**, **anti-** and **re-**.

a) _____ star

b) _____ write

c) _____ clockwise

d) _____ charge

e) _____ power

f) _____ biotic

g) _____ cycle

h) _____ septic

i) _____ natural

4 Read these words which have the prefix **un-**, **dis-**, **mis-**, **super-**, **anti-** or **re-**. Tick the ones which are real words and put a cross next to the words that are made up.

reappear	✓	dispencil	✗
misbehave		antiuncle	
unfair		untable	
misread		reform	
supermoney		misruler	
retype		unequal	

How did I do?

 ☐   ☐   ☐

23

Using determiners

A **determiner** stands before a singular noun and any other words which explain the noun.

Here are some of the most common determiners, which are also known as articles:

> the, a, an

Deciding whether to use a or an

a	an
When words begin with a consonant.	When words begin with a vowel.
a girl a rabbit a pencil a street a house	an elephant an igloo an apple an umbrella an orange

WARMING UP

 1 Read the words below and decide whether to use the determiner **a** or **an**.

a) .... balloon   b) .... car

c) .... robot   d) .... mango

e) .... egg   f) .... ant

g) .... ice cream   h) .... octopus

i) .... kettle

Using determiners

GETTING HOTTER

2 Here are some more examples of determiners. Choose one to complete each sentence.

another	other	this	both	my

a) _____ Dylan and Daniel wanted an ice cream.

b) I don't like this. Can I have _____ one please?

c) This drink is mine and the _____ one is Mum's.

d) _____ is my new car.

e) I really like _____ new haircut.

BURN IT UP!

3 Read these sentences and underline the determiners.

a) I would like either an apple or a pear.

b) Both singers were very good tonight.

c) The other bike was much faster.

d) His school report was not very good.

e) How was your holiday?

How did I do?

 ☐   ☐   ☐

Using time conjunctions

Time conjunctions are used to show that time is passing or has passed.

Here are some for you to try and use in your writing:

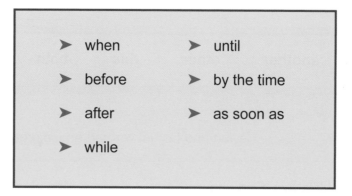

➤ when   ➤ until

➤ before   ➤ by the time

➤ after   ➤ as soon as

➤ while

WARMING UP

 1 Read these sentences. Underline the correct conjunction to complete each one.

a) I promise I will phone you **when / until** I get there.

b) All of the cakes had gone **by the time / while** I got to the party.

c) Freddie waited at the station **until / as soon as** the diesel train arrived.

d) **Before / as soon as** I go to bed I will brush my teeth.

e) I will play cards with you **after / by the time** I have had my bath.

How did I do?

 ☐   ☐   ☐

26

Using adverbs of time

We can also use adverbs in our sentences to show time is passing or has passed.

WARMING UP

 1 Some of these adverbs have missing letters. Complete them to make an adverb.

ne___t (x or a) = next

a) so___n (o or i) _____

b) t___en (k or h) _____

c) toda___ (e or y) _____

d) dur___ng (i or a) _____

e) recent___y (l or e) _____

GETTING HOTTER

 2 Read these sentences and circle the adverbs of time.

a) I'm going to school soon.

b) Would you like to go next?

c) Yesterday I bought a new school bag.

d) I woke up five times during the night.

e) We've been to the zoo today.

How did I do?

 ☐   ☐   ☐

27

What is a preposition?

A preposition links nouns or pronouns to another word in the sentence.

The preposition comes at the beginning of the phrase. It usually tells the reader where the object is.

in the garden	**on top** of the world
up the mountain	**after** breakfast
with his friend	**through** the forest
round the corner	**under** the bridge
over the hill	**inside** the house

Read the following sentences, the prepositions tell us where the cat is.

The cat is **on** the mat.

The cat is **next to** the mat.

The cat sat **under** the mat.

The cat sat **beside** the mat.

The cat sat **behind** the mat.

The cat sat **beneath** the mat.

WARMING UP

 1 Choose a preposition to complete the sentences below.

next to	onto	under	through

a) Claire climbed .... the boat.

b) Claire slept .... the stars.

c) Claire stood .... James.

d) Claire ran .... the garden with Lennie.

How did I do? ☐ ☐ ☐

Using prepositions accurately

We can also use prepositions in sentences to introduce and connect ideas:

before **during**

after **because of**

following **except**

 Choose a preposition to complete the sentences below. Use the prepositions above to help you.

a) _____ he knew it, the door had slammed shut in front of him.

b) _____ the night, all of the animals escaped from their cages.

c) _____ the argument Joey left the park and ran home.

d) Everybody passed the test _____ me.

e) _____ the discussion, I knew exactly what to do.

f) The houses were ruined _____ the recent floods.

How did I do?

 ☐   ☐   ☐

Assess and review

1 Add the correct prefix to these words. Use un-, dis-, mis-, super-, anti- or re-.

a) _____ behave   b) _____ natural

c) _____ decided   d) _____ turn

e) _____ tie   f) _____ pay

g) _____ move   h) _____ continue

i) _____ fill   j) _____ freeze

k) _____ take   l) _____ play

GETTING HOTTER

2 Add **a** or **an** to each of the following nouns:

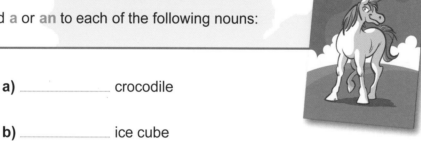

a) _____ crocodile

b) _____ ice cube

c) _____ island   d) _____ packet

e) _____ eagle   f) _____ train

g) _____ motorbike   h) _____ computer

i) _____ unicorn   j) _____ owl

k) _____ alligator   l) _____ holiday

3 Choose a conjunction to complete each sentence.

when	as soon as	after
until		before

a) I want to comb my hair _____ I go out.

b) I will wait here _____ the shop opens.

c) I will wash the dishes _____ the film has finished.

d) I slept for an hour _____ the party started.

BURN IT UP!

4 How many prepositions can you remember? Try to write down ten.

How did I do?

 ☐   ☐   ☐

Titles and subheadings

Titles

When we pick up a book and read its title, we immediately create a picture in our minds of what this book may be about. For example, The Three Little Pigs implies that the story will be about three little pigs.

Titles:

- ✓ are short and snappy,
- ✓ are written to hook the reader in,
- ✓ sometimes include alliteration (**W**innie the **W**itch).

WARMING UP

 1 Match the titles and the extracts. One has been done for you.

Titles	Extracts
All About Drumming	**a)** London is the capital city of England and has many exciting attractions for tourists.
The Unhappiest Princess	**b)** On 3rd January, scientists discovered an unusual duckling with the strangest collection of feathers!
Ugly Duckling?	**c)** There are many different types of drums in the world: kettle, bongo and steel are just a few.
A Guide to London	**d)** In a land further away than you can imagine lived Princess Hope. Her short life of 8 years had been full of misery.

Titles and subheadings

Subheadings

Subheadings:

   ✓   are usually used to organise non-fiction texts, such as reports, explanations and instructions,

   ✓   are used to separate the text in a piece of writing,

   ✓   are sometimes underlined or written in capital letters.

For example, if you were writing a report about your school, you might use the following subheadings:

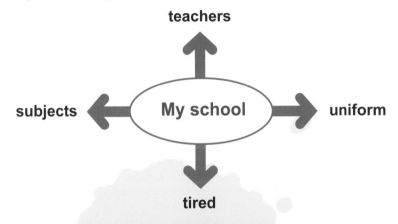

GETTING HOTTER

 2 Here is some information about a rabbit. Write the subheading for each piece of information.

a) ....   b) ....   c) ....

....

....

| Rabbits usually live in hutches when they are pets. You will need to change their hay regularly. | Rabbits eat a mixture of flakes which can be bought from pet shops. They drink water too. | Rabbits need to exercise daily so you will need to allow them to run around in the garden. They like to burrow too. |

How did I do?   ☐   ☐   ☐

How do we organise our writing?

All writing needs to be organised so that the reader can understand what is written.

There are many different ways to organise our thoughts. Before we actually write anything we should plan our ideas.

Once we have planned what we want to write, we must organise our thoughts by using words and phrases. These then act like signposts, helping the reader to follow our thoughts.

Sometimes it is obvious from the opening to the sentence whether we are reading the beginning or the ending of a story.

'Once upon a time' is a traditional opening to a story. 'And they all lived happily ever after' is a traditional ending for a story.

WARMING UP

 1 Write **O** for opening and **E** for ending next to these phrases.

> **a)** one bright sunny day ....
>
> **b)** early one morning ....
>
> **c)** and everything worked out for the best ....
>
> **d)** so life would never be the same again ....

How do we organise our writing?

Using paragraphs

All good stories have a beginning, a middle and an ending. We must organise our writing into these sections so that each section can be represented by a new paragraph.

Starting a new paragraph shows the reader that the character, place, topic or time may be changed.

 2 Read the sections below, decide what order they should be read in and then number them. The title has been done for you.

	a) Humpty Dumpty sat on the wall.
	b) All the king's horses and all the king's men couldn't put Humpty together again.
1	**Humpty Dumpty**
	c) Humpty Dumpty had a great fall.

How did I do?

 ☐ ☐ ☐

Using pronouns to vary the subject

Cara was really excited about starting ballet lessons. Cara had looked forward to this day. Cara put Cara's ballet kit in Cara's new bag. Cara was ready to go and Cara was excited.

When we write sentences, we need to use pronouns to vary the subject. Pronouns replace nouns. Here are some pronouns: me, him, his, she, he, her, who, what, that.

1 Use pronouns to complete these sentences.

> Cara was really excited about starting ballet lessons. _____
>
> had looked forward to this day. _____ put _____
>
> ballet kit in _____ new bag. Cara was ready to go and
>
> _____ was excited.

2 Underline the correct pronoun to complete each of these sentences.

a) Jacob put his shoes on by himself / his.

b) Mum and Dad bought her / she a new phone.

c) Everybody blames me / my for everything.

d) I wonder if he / me will score a goal.

How did I do?

Introducing dialogue

In fiction characters talk to each other. Dialogue is the conversation they are having with other characters.

We can use speech bubbles in comic strips and illustrations. However, when we write dialogue in a story we need to use speech marks.

> "Hey, how are you doing?"
>
> "I'm having a great day. How are you?"

We also need to report **who** is speaking.

> "Hey, how are you doing?" asked **Prince Charming**.
>
> "I'm having a great day. How are you?" replied **Cinderella**.

There are many verbs we can use to show **how** the character speaks:

> **whispered**   **muttered**   **answered**
>
>   **said**   **responded**
>   **smiled**
>
> **shouted**
>   **screamed**   **mumbled**

Punctuating direct speech

> **"Don't go into the forest Little Red Riding Hood,"** said Mum.

This is an example of direct speech.

Direct speech is what the speaker actually says.

There are some rules to punctuate direct speech:

➤ each new speaker goes on a new line

➤ speech marks " " go around the direct speech

➤ a comma goes between direct speech and the name of the person who has spoken

➤ no comma is used if the direct speech has an ! or a ?

➤ direct speech begins with a capital letter.

> **"What big eyes you have Grandma!"**
> said Little Red Riding Hood.
>
> **"All the better to see you with,"**
> whispered the wolf.

 Punctuate the sentences below by putting the speech marks around the direct speech.

a) What big teeth you have Grandma! said Little Red Riding Hood.

b) All the better to eat you with! screamed the wolf.

Punctuating direct speech

2 There are some mistakes in the sentences below. Rewrite them using the correct punctuation.

a) "What would you like to eat for lunch? asked Mum.

_____

_____

b) "I would like a ham, cheese and tomato sandwich" please Mum said Kirsty.

_____

_____

c) Your sandwich is ready Kirsty, come and get it please "called Mum."

_____

_____

_____

d) Thanks Mum, you are the best!" smiled Kirsty.

_____

_____

How did I do?

 ☐   ☐   ☐

Present perfect form of verbs

When we want to write about something that has happened in the past, but we do not specify the time, we use the **present perfect tense**.

> We take the past participle of the verb and then add the verb **have** before it.

I **have** been to India.

> I **have** done my homework already.
>
> He **has** scored three goals by half time.
>
> **Have** you ever met the head teacher?
>
> You **have** grown so much this year.

WARMING UP

 1 Underline the present perfect tense in these sentences.

a) He has never been to a theme park.

b) The rain hasn't stopped all day.

c) I have had so much to eat today.

d) We have had three tests this week already.

Present perfect form of verbs

2 Complete these sentences.

a) I (**visit**) _____ _____ Wales before.

b) She (**visit**) _____ _____ Wales before.

c) The police (**arrest**) _____ _____ three men today.

d) The ice (**melt**) _____ _____ because of the sun.

Some verbs are irregular and we need to learn them.
For example, the verb **to eat**:

Laura **has eaten** her lunch already.

Laura and John **have eaten** their lunch already.

3 Complete these sentences.

a) Sarah (**write**) _____ _____ two letters.

b) It (**be**) _____ _____ a great week.

c) David and Carlos (**take**) _____ _____ penalties today.

d) Nicole (**ride**) _____ _____ horses since she was very young.

e) My family and I (**go**) _____ _____ to Ireland many times.

f) I (**take**) _____ _____ the dog for a walk already.

How did I do?   ☐   ☐   ☐

41

Conjunctions and connectives

There are many different ways to open paragraphs and sequence ideas in our writing.

We can use connectives and conjunctions like these:

first	next	then	after that	so
eventually	finally	when	one day	it all began
at last	it was the end	yesterday	without warning	in a flash

 Organise the connectives and conjunctions above into the places you would expect to use them in a story. Some have been done for you.

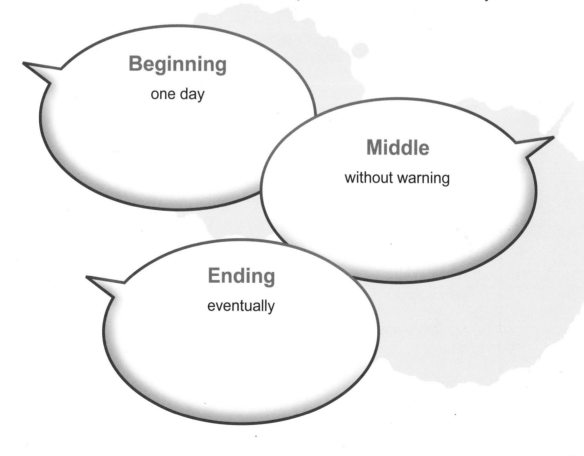

Beginning
one day

Middle
without warning

Ending
eventually

How did I do?

Assess and review

1 Correct these sentences using the correct punctuation for direct speech.

---

a) My legs are really hurting cried Nadien.

....

....

b) I want to go and see the train at the station said Freddie.

....

....

c) Come on, let's go out and play exclaimed Bal.

....

....

d) Somebody help, please, HELP! screamed the old lady.

....

....

GETTING HOTTER

2 Circle the word which is a pronoun in each line.

a)	he	door	cat
b)	book	my	house
c)	they	table	because
d)	until	her	clock
e)	during	in	your
f)	cake	pen	his

43

Assess and review

BURN IT UP!

3 Use the present perfect form to complete these sentences. **Don't forget to add the verb** have.

---

a) I (see) _____ _____ this film before.

b) My Mum (wash) _____ _____ my clothes for me.

c) He (finish) _____ _____ his homework before everybody else.

d) She (visit) _____ _____ Greece before.

e) Dad (cook) _____ _____ dinner for everybody.

f) The florist (arrange) _____ _____ the wedding flowers beautifully.

g) We (know) _____ _____ the Flanagans for years.

h) I (wait) _____ _____ over an hour for a bus.

How did I do?

 ☐   ☐   ☐

44